TI
PUSH

FOREWORD

In case anyone wonders, Rosamund Cozens-Cugat is a pseudonym.

Pushkin was real. He died in mysterious circumstances while still a very young cat, and this little book was begun as a memorial to him. It also disappeared in mysterious circumstances, more than once, and is now anxiously published before it also runs out of lives. It is meant to entertain the captive grown-up reader as well as the child-on-knee.

It just grew, and it was disconcerting to perceive the shadowy likenesses of friends and acquaintances emerging in the little feline faces and characters - good reason for the pseudonym.

So, here it is, some thirty-five years on, and thanks to the encouragement of my family and to the patience shown by Wilton 65.

R. C-C.

Published in 1995
by
WILTON 65
Flat Top House, Bishop Wilton, York. YO4 1RY

ISBN 0947828 33 8

Printed & bound by
Bourne Press, Bournemouth

For Mother

without whose annual enquiries

this book never would have been

finished .

THE PUSHKINS

A Tale of Cats with a Kink
or
A Scatirical Romance

By Rosamund Cozens-Cugat

The Pushkins came from a remarkable family of Siamese cats. For hundreds of years they had adorned the office of Cats Extraordinary to the Kings of Siam.

They had kinks in their tails where their royal masters used to twist them between their fingers while they were thinking deeply about affairs of State, and they had crossed eyes from looking down their noses at everyone else.

5.

This story begins in 1909, when one of the younger sons of the House decided to go abroad. He was bored with the Palace, where indeed his prospects were poor, and wanted to see something of the world for himself. This was Ki-Ting, (so-named by Anna). He travelled incognito —

and it took one hundred coolies to carry his luggage.

He went by way of Suez,

Port Said,

and Venice, and though loath
to quit that city of languid
patrician pleasures

he continued across the Continent

to Russia. He went first to Moscow, and was at once captivated by all things Russian, quickly applying himself to learning the language and taking the name Pushkin. He later settled in

St Petersburg where he had
an introduction to Prince
Pussopov, and for a time
became involved in political
intrigue and the plots to kill
Ratsputin.

This sort of thing, however, was not so much to his taste as caviare, vodka, and the Bolshoi, and in 1916 he met Mimi Mauskatcha, a very beautiful Circatsian who was a member of the corps de ballet. She was more distinguished

for her beauty than her
dancing, and as it was a
case of true love it was not
long before Ki-Jing persuaded
her to retire and they were
married. None of the Diplomatic
Corps attended the Ceremony, nor
was the Court of Siam represented.

Mimi was a White Russian and at the outbreak of the Revolution they fled — with only the clothes they stood up in — and the samovar.

After many days of anxious travel they reached Paris, where they were to experience great poverty, and where

Mimi soon died, quite worn
out, poor thing.

Ki-Ting was left with a
small son. They had named
him Felix.

After Mimi's death Ki-Ting
sold her sapphire necklace
(a gift from the Tsar) and
bought a taxicab.

Within a few years he owned
a whole fleet of taxis, and

was able to send Felix to
an English public School (where
he did not particularly
distinguish himself) and then

to Cambridge University —
(Cat's, of course). Felix
soon found he was not
one of the narrower
academic types,

and as he proved an
unduly disturbing influence
on College life

he was sent down.

He then played the guitar
for a time with Kats Wauber
and his Band.
When his father discovered
this, he very quickly sent

him out to Kenya with a small,
but regular, remittance. He took
a job as Manager on a sisal
estate belonging to a retired
General, Thomas Foulis-Rattrick.

He was a widower with an only daughter, Farida. She was half Persian and very beautiful.

Felix found her shy and aloof.

He adored her from afar,
and in desperation and
despair he took to drink.

Before long he went down
with fever, and this brought
Farida to his aid. She nursed
him devotedly, and

when Felix felt better they came

rapidly to an understanding.

Tom Rattrick said they might

marry when Felix had planted

1000 acres of sisal. This not

only gave Ki-Ting time to come

out for the wedding, but was

the foundation of the vast family fortune when sisal boomed a few years later. Ki-Ting got on so well with the General that he was easily persuaded to make Kenya his home. It was a country where everyone had room to be themselves, only more so.

Ki-Jing suspected Farida's loveliness was matched only by her stupidity — in fact he was satisfied she would suit Felix admirably,

as indeed she did, and they
lived happily ever after.

Ki-Zing rather took to his grandson, Pushkin.

He was a stolid child, and it was difficult to see quite where his charm lay.

His parents waited patiently
for signs of genius to appear.
Farida consoled herself more
and more with his pretty
sister, Anna.

Ki-Jing thought Pushkin's rare bursts of activity entirely misdirected.

Tom Rattrick gave him a gun for his twelfth birthday.

Up to that time there had been only two things Pushkin liked doing — eating and sleeping. Now he began to take his gun out into the bush and come home with that far-horizons look in his eyes.

So when he grew up, he became a White Hunter, and confounded everyone by making a success of it.

For years he thought
only of trophies, until
at last he met

Didimoushka!

Didi was one of those who learn the hard way — joyfully. She tried everything once, and found life correspondingly full of surprises.

She was a war orphan, and had been brought down from Siberia in a Red Cross lorry, after the Yiawlta Agreement,

and after a spell in camps
in the Middle East was sent
to Kenya to be brought up
in a Mission. But she
was a sly puss, and when

she went to work in Nairobi

she rapidly blossomed out.

She began using too much

make-up and putting scent

behind her ears (also too

much). She loved it.

Pushkin met her in a night club. They were soon dancing cheek to cheek and Pushkin was utterly overcome by Didi — and Chatnelle No. 5.

But Didimoushka had numbers of eager admirers, in particular a tough farmer from the Cateaux District, called de Fliess. Pushkin loathed him, and there followed some strenuous months of courtship for them all.

Didi adored every minute of it, but discovered just in time that it was Pushkin she really loved. (Engagement Photograph).

They spent their honeymoon on a Big Game Safari. Pushkin determined that in future Didi would have to stay at home.

Didimoushka decided
Pushkin should retire and
take up farming.

Ki~ting bought them an estate in the foothills of Mount Kenya, where they intended ranching beef for export to the Persian Gulf. (Farida still had useful connections in that part of the world).

Very soon Didi (like a good many other people who never had one) quite pined for a good old-fashioned English Nanny. She was delightfully absorbed with her young family and they seemed all set for a long and happy life.

Pushkin liked an occasional evening stroll. But one day he went too near the forest

and was ambushed by
Miau Miau gangsters.

He didn't stand a chance.